Contents

OXFORD
UNIVERSITY PRESS

Great Clarendon Street, Oxford, OX2 6DP, United Kingdom

Oxford University Press is a department of the University
of Oxford. It furthers the University's objective of excellence
in research, scholarship, and education by publishing
worldwide. Oxford is a registered trade mark of Oxford
University Press in the UK and in certain other countries

British Library Cataloguing in Publication Data
Data available

ISBN: 978-0-19-276476-8

10

Paper used in the production of this book is a natural, recyclable product
made from wood grown in sustainable forests. The manufacturing process
conforms to the environmental regulations of the country of origin.

Printed in Great Britain by Bell and Bain Ltd, Glasgow

Acknowledgements

Series Editor: Clare Kirtley

Cover illustration by Deborah Allwright

Top Cat and *Cat Naps* illustrated by Joelle Dreidemy

Sam's Pot illustrated by Pauline Siewert

Bob Bug, Mum Bug's Bag and *Mix, Mix, Mix* illustrated by Deborah Allwright

The Big Cod illustrated by Andy Hammond

Pen Fun illustrated by Judy Brown

The Pins and the Pegs illustrated by Jenny Williams

Is It? illustrated by Deborah Allwright, Joelle Dreidemy, Andy Hammond
and Alan Marks

Julia Donaldson's Songbirds

Practising phonics

Phonics is a method of teaching children to recognise words by focusing on the sounds of language. Children learn to recognise letter patterns and learn the sounds they represent, in order to sound out words to read.

The **Songbirds phonics story books** introduce letter patterns and sounds gradually and systematically, providing your child with highly decodable texts which can be read by sounding out and blending. They provide the perfect reading context for your child to build up and practise a secure knowledge of phonics.

The carefully structured way in which the **Songbirds phonics story books** introduce the complexities of phonics maximises your child's success at reading. The stories begin by introducing children to the sounds made by single letters, move on to the sounds made by pairs of letters and finally introduce children to the concept that the same sound can be written in more than one way. This is all done through lively stories, written by award-winning author, Julia Donaldson.

Helping your child to read

Children learn best when they are relaxed and having fun. Encourage your child to point to and say the sound made by each letter pattern listed at the start of a story. This will equip your child with the necessary knowledge to confidently and successfully read the phonic words in the story. Remember to give your child lots of praise as they read to build their confidence.

After reading a story, encourage your child to reflect on the main events and to retell the story to develop his or her comprehension. Help your child to find words containing the letter patterns listed at the start of the story. Ask your child to read these words, to look at the letter patterns in them and then to have a go at spelling them. Your child can have fun practising their phonics knowledge further by completing the supporting phonics activities in the accompanying **Songbirds** *My Phonics Activity Book* at Stage 1. There are four **Songbirds** activity books at Stage 1 to Stage 4.

More on **oxfordowl.co.uk**
Practical advice, free eBooks and fun activities to help your child progress.
Let's get them flying!

4

Top Cat

Tips for reading Top Cat together

This story practises these sounds:

a t p m o c

Ask your child to point to each of these letters and say the sound
(e.g. *c* as in *cat*, not the letter name *cee*). Look out for these letters
in the story.

Your child might find this word tricky:

I

Explain that this is a very common word, but you do not sound it out.
Say the word for your child if they do not know it.

Before you begin, ask your child to read the title by sounding out first
(say each letter out loud, e.g. *t-o-p*) and then blending the word together
(e.g. *top*). Look at the picture together. What do you think this story is
about?

Remind your child to read unfamiliar words by saying the individual
sounds and then blending them together quickly to read the word. When
you have finished reading the story, look through it again and:

- Talk about the cats' expressions on each page. Ask your child, *How do
  they feel?*

- Find the words that end with the *p* sound (*top, pop*). Notice that they
  sound the same at the end of the word. Have fun thinking of some
  other words that rhyme with *top* and *pop* (*mop, hop, shop, flop, chop,
  stop*).

I am top cat.

Am I top cat?

I am! I am!

I am top cat.

Am I top cat?

I am! I am!

Am I top cat?

Sam's Pot

Tips for reading Sam's Pot together

This story practises these sounds:

s m c t g p a o

Ask your child to point to each of these letters and say the sound (e.g. *m* as in *mum*, not the letter name *em*). Look out for these letters in the story.

Before you begin, ask your child to read the title by sounding out first (say each letter out loud, e.g. *p-o-t*) and then blending the word together (e.g. *pot*). Look at the picture together. What do you think this story is about?

Remind your child to read unfamiliar words by saying the individual sounds and then blending them together quickly to read the word. When you have finished reading the story, look through it again and:

- Ask your child, *Why did Tom get a mop?* Talk about what Sam is doing on each page.

- Find the words that begin with the *t* sound (*Tom, tap*). Does the *t* sound look the same in all of these words? Talk about capital letters and how they are used for names and at the beginning of sentences. Find some more words that begin with capital letters (*Pam, Sam*). Ask your child, *What sound does the capital letter make in these words?*

Tom got a pot.

Pam got a pot.

Sam got a pot.

Pat, pat, pat!

Tom

A cat

Tap, tap, tap!
Tap, tap, tap!

Tom got a mop!

Bob Bug

Tips for reading Bob Bug together

This story practises these sounds:

r l d b f h i u s

m c t g p a o

Ask your child to point to each of these letters and say the sound (e.g. *u* as in *umbrella*, not the letter name *yoo*). Look out for these letters in the story.

Before you begin, ask your child to read the title by sounding out first (say each letter out loud, e.g. *b-u-g*) and then blending the word together (e.g. *bug*). Look at the picture together. What do you think this story is about?

Remind your child to read unfamiliar words by saying the individual sounds and then blending them together quickly to read the word. When you have finished reading the story, look through it again and:

- Ask your child, *Do you think there really was a rat in Bob Bug's bedroom? How do you know?*

- Find the words that begin with the *b* sound (*Bob, Bug, big, bad*). Does the *b* sound look the same in all of these words? Talk about capital letters and how they are used for names and at the beginning of sentences. Find some more words that begin with capital letters (*Mum, Dad*). Ask your child, *What sound does the capital letter make in these words?*

Bob is a bug.

Bob Bug has a mum. His mum is big.

Bob has a dad. His dad is fit.

Bob has a cup. It has a lid.

Bob has a cot. His cot has a rug.

33

Bob Bug has a hug.

Dig, Dig, Dig!

Tips for reading Dig, Dig, Dig! together

This story practises these sounds:

r l d b f h i u s

m t g p a o n

Ask your child to point to each of these letters and say the sound
(e.g. *r* as in *rabbit*, not the letter name *ar*). Look out for these letters
in the story.

Your child might find this word tricky:

of

Explain that this word is common, but the *f* in *of* is unusual and makes the
v sound. Say the word for your child if they do not know it.

Before you begin, ask your child to read the title by sounding out first (say each
letter out loud, e.g. *d-i-g*) and then blending the word together (e.g. *dig*). Look at
the picture together. What do you think this story is about?

Remind your child to read unfamiliar words by saying the individual sounds and
then blending them together quickly to read the word. When you have finished
reading the story, look through it again and:

- Talk about Tim and the dog on the last page, are they disappointed? Ask your
  child, *What did Tim think would be inside the tin?*

- Find the words that begin with the *l* sound (*lot, lid, lots*). Point to the middle
  letter in *lid* and ask your child, *What sound does this letter make?* Find more
  words with the *i* sound in the middle (*dig, Tim, his, big*). Have fun thinking of
  some other words with the *i* sound in the middle (*wig, him, bin, fit*).

Dig, dig, dig!
Tim and his dog had fun.

Dig, dig, dig!
Tim dug up a lot of mud.

Dig, dig, dig!
His dog dug up a rag.

Dig, dig, dig!
Tim dug up a bus.

Dig, dig, dig!
A lid!

Dig, dig, dig!
A big tin!

And in it. . .

lots of bugs!

Zak and the Vet

Tips for reading Zak and the Vet together

This story practises these sounds:

v w y z j n k e r d b
f h i u s m c t g a o

Ask your child to point to each of these letters and say the sound (e.g. *v* as in *van*, not the letter name *vee*). Look out for these letters in the story.

Your child might find these words tricky:

better he the to will

These words are common, but your child may not have learned how to sound them out yet. Say the words for your child if they do not know them.

Before you begin, ask your child to read the title by sounding out first (say each letter out loud, e.g. *Z-a-k*) and then blending the word together (e.g. *Zak*). Look at the picture together. What do you think this story is about?

Remind your child to read unfamiliar words by saying the individual sounds and then blending them together quickly to read the word. When you have finished reading the story, look through it again and:

- Ask your child, *Who helped Zak?* Talk about what a vet is.
- Find the words that begin with the *v* sound (*van, vet*). Point to the *e* in *vet*. What sound does this make? Find some other words in the book with *e* in the middle (*red, Jen, get, yes*).

Zak did not sit. Zak ran.

Zak ran in the fog.
A red van hit him.

Jen and Zak went to the vet.

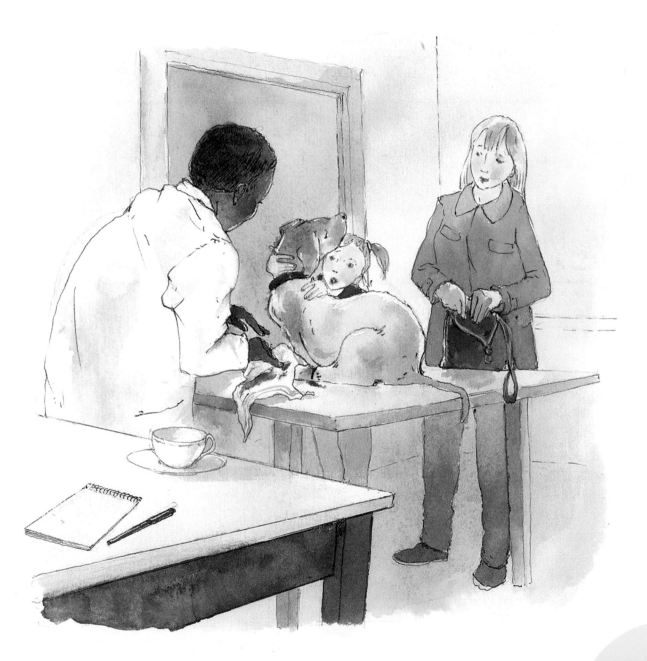

Zak had a bad cut. He had to get a jab.

Will Zak get better?

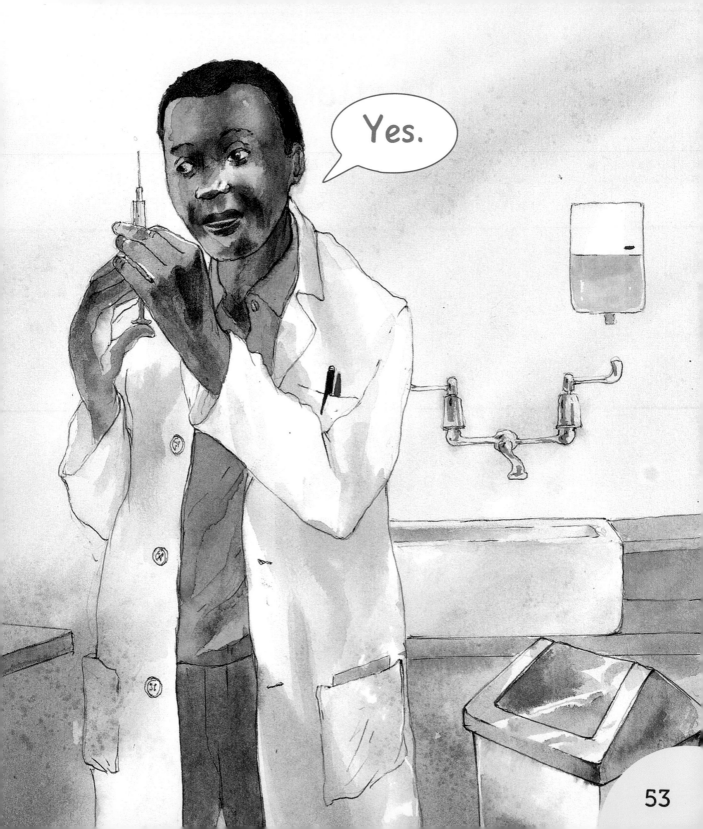

53

Zak did get better.

wag wag wag

Mum Bug's Bag

Tips for reading Mum Bug's Bag together

This story practises these sounds:

w y z j n k e r d b f
h i u s m c t g p a o

Ask your child to point to each of these letters and say the sound (e.g. *j* as in *jug*, not the letter name *jay*). Look out for these letters in the story.

Your child might find these words tricky:

her   of   the   hole

These words are common, but your child may not have learned how to sound them out yet. Say the words for your child if they do not know them.

Before you begin, ask your child to read the title by sounding out first (say each letter out loud, e.g. *M-u-m*) and then blending the word together (e.g. *Mum*). Look at the picture together. What do you think this story is about?

Remind your child to read unfamiliar words by saying the individual sounds and then blending them together quickly to read the word. When you have finished reading the story, look through it again and:

- Ask your child, *What fell out of Mum Bug's bag?*
- Find the words that end with the *n* sound (*can, pen, fan, bun*). Notice the *u* in *bun*. Find other words in the book with the *u* sound in the middle (*Mum, Yuk, bug*). Have fun thinking of some other words with the *u* sound in the middle (*hum, hug, rug, run*).

Mum Bug has a red bag.
The bag has a zip.

Mum can fit a pen in her bag.

Mum can fit a pen and
a fan in her bag.

Mum can fit a pen and
a fan and
a bun in her bag.

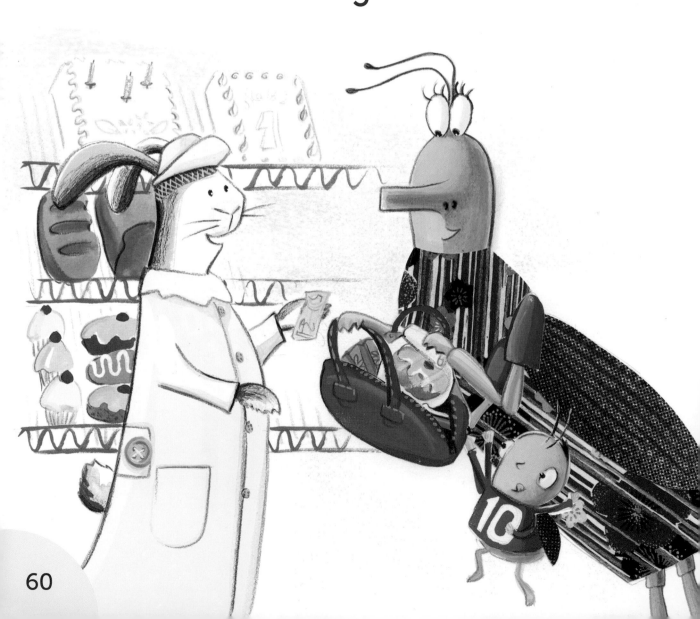

Mum can fit a pen and
a fan and
a bun and
a pot of jam in her bag.

Mum has a hole in her bag!

The pen and
the fan and
the bun and
the jam get wet.

Mum Bug gets a big bag.

Cat Naps

Tips for reading Cat Naps together

This story practises these sounds:

a b c d e g h i k m
n o p r s t u v w y

Ask your child to point to each of these letters and say the sound (e.g. *b* as in *bug*, not the letter name *bee*). Look out for these letters in the story.

Your child might find these words tricky:

of and it's

These words are common, but your child may not have learned how to sound them out yet. Say the words for your child if they do not know them.

Before you begin, ask your child to read the title by sounding out first (say each letter out loud, e.g. *c-a-t*) and then blending the word together (e.g. *cat*). Look at the picture together. What do you think this story is about?

Remind your child to read unfamiliar words by saying the individual sounds and then blending them together quickly to read the word. When you have finished reading the story, look through it again and:

- Talk about what Kit Cat might be thinking on page 70.
- Find the words that end with the *p* sound (*top, nap, cap*). Notice that *cap* and *nap* sound the same at the end because they rhyme. Have fun thinking of some other words that rhyme with *nap* and *cap* (*tap, map, lap, gap*).

Top Cat had a nap in a cap.

Kit Cat had a nap in a sun hat.

Top Cat had a nap in a big top hat.

Kit Cat had a nap on a mat.
Top Cat had a nap on a rug.

Kit Cat had a nap in a cot.
Top Cat had a nap on a bed.

Pad pad pad! Wag wag wag!
Yap yap yap!

It's a dog! Run, Top Cat!
Run, Kit Cat!

Top Cat and Kit Cat had a nap on top of a van.

Pen Fun

Tips for reading Pen Fun together

This story practises these sounds:

a b d e f g i j k l m
n o p r s t u v w z

Ask your child to point to each of these letters and say the sound (e.g. *b* as in *bug*, not the letter name *bee*). Look out for these letters in the story.

Your child might find these words tricky:

of gives the to

These words are common, but your child may not have learned how to sound them out yet. Say the words for your child if they do not know them.

Before you begin, ask your child to read the title by sounding out first (say each letter out loud, e.g. *p-e-n*) and then blending the word together (e.g. *pen*). Look at the picture together. What do you think this story is about?

Remind your child to read unfamiliar words by saying the individual sounds and then blending them together quickly to read the word. When you have finished reading the story, look through it again and:

- Ask your child if they think pens are a good present and why.

- Find a word that begins with the *j* sound (*Jez*). Talk about capital letters and how they are used for names and at the beginning of sentences. Find some more words that begin with capital letters (*Rod, Pip, Edwin, Meg, Kev, Dot*). Ask your child, *What sound does the capital letter make in these words?*

Rod has a pen.

Pip has a big pen.

Edwin has a big fat pen.

Meg has a big fat red pen.

Kev has a big fat red fun pen.

Dot has a set of big fat red fun pens.

Jez has ten sets of big fat red fun pens!

Jez gives the pen sets to his pals.

The Big Cod

Tips for reading The Big Cod together

This story practises these sounds:

a b c d e g i m
n o r s t u w y

Ask your child to point to each of these letters and say the sound
(e.g. *d* as in *dog*, not the letter name *dee*). Look out for these letters
in the story.

Your child might find these words tricky:

the   and   Tim's

These words are common, but your child may not have learned how to
sound them out yet. Say the words for your child if they do not know them.

Before you begin, ask your child to read the title by sounding out first (say each
letter out loud, e.g. *c-o-d*) and then blending the word together (e.g. *cod*). Look
at the picture together. What do you think this story is about?

Remind your child to read unfamiliar words by saying the individual sounds
and then blending them together quickly to read the word. When you have
finished reading the story, look through it again and:

- Talk about if you would rather use a fishing net or a fishing rod
  and why.

- Find some words in the story that end with the *t* sound (*net, sit, it,
  bit, wet*). Read each word by sounding out and blending. Which
  of these words rhyme? Think of other words that rhyme with *net*
  and *wet* (*bet, get, jet, let, met, pet, set, vet*).

Tim has a net and a can.

Tim's Dad has a rod and a can.

Tim and Dad sit and sit.

Dad tugs and tugs.

The cod tugs and tugs.

Dad gets wet.

The Pins and the Pegs

Tips for reading The Pins and the Pegs together

This story practises these sounds:

a b d e f g h j l m
n o p r s t u v

Ask your child to point to each of these letters and say the sound (e.g. *v* as in *van*, not the letter name *vee*). Look out for these letters in the story.

Your child might find these words tricky:

of was the I put let's and

These words are common, but your child may not have learned how to sound them out yet. Say the words for your child if they do not know them.

Before you begin, ask your child to read the title by sounding out first (say each letter out loud, e.g. *p-i-n-s*) and then blending the word together (e.g. *pins*). Look at the picture together. What do you think this story is about?

Remind your child to read unfamiliar words by saying the individual sounds and then blending them together quickly to read the word. When you have finished reading the story, look through it again and:

- Talk about why Val was confused (*the pins and the pegs had moved by themselves*).

- Shut the book, then say all the sounds in *bin* separately, and then write the letter that makes each of those sounds. Change one letter to write the word *bun*, then *ban*.

Val had a bag of pegs.

Val had a tin of pins.

Val was in bed.

The pins and the pegs got up.

The pins and the pegs had fun.

Val got up.

The pins and the pegs
ran and hid.

Is It?

Tips for reading Is It? together

This story practises these sounds:

a b c d e f g i j m
n o p r s t u v w y

Ask your child to point to each of these letters and say the sound (e.g. *p* as in *pet*, not the letter name *pee*). Look out for these letters in the story.

Your child might find these words tricky:

what the who Bug's it's Tim's

These words are common, but your child may not have learned how to sound them out yet. Say the words for your child if they do not know them.

Before you begin, ask your child to read the title by sounding out first (say each letter out loud, e.g. *b-a-g*) and then blending the word together (e.g. *bag*). Look at the picture together. What do you think this story is about?

Remind your child to read unfamiliar words by saying the individual sounds and then blending them together quickly to read the word. When you have finished reading the story, look through it again and:

- Ask your child, *Where was Top Cat? Why do you think he was hiding there?*

- Read page 113 and find the two words that rhyme (*cat*, *rat*). Have fun thinking of other words that rhyme with *cat* and *rat* (*mat, hat, bat, sat, pat*). Try to write some of the words. Say all of the sounds in the word separately then write the letter that makes each sound.

What is in Mum Bug's bag?

Is it a wig? Is it a fan?
Is it a jug?

Yes, it's a jug!

What is in the fog?

Is it a van? Is it a bus?
Is it a jet?

Yes, it's a bus!

Who is in the mud?

Is it Tim? Is it Tim's Dad?
Is it Tim's dog?

Yes, it's Tim!

Who is in bed?

Is it a cat? Is it a dog?
Is it a rat?

Yes, it's a cat! It's Top Cat!

Mix, Mix, Mix

Tips for reading Mix, Mix, Mix together

This story practises these sounds:

a b c d e f g i j k l
m n o p r s t u x y

Ask your child to point to each of these letters and say the sound (e.g. *y* as in *yum*, not the letter name *why*). Look out for these letters in the story.

Your child might find these words tricky:

of   says   and

These words are common, but your child may not have learned how to sound them out yet. Say the words for your child if they do not know them.

Before you begin, ask your child to read the title by sounding out first (say each letter out loud, e.g. *m-i-x*) and then blending the word together (e.g. *mix*). Look at the picture together. What do you think this story is about?

Remind your child to read unfamiliar words by saying the individual sounds and then blending them together quickly to read the word. When you have finished reading the story, look through it again and:

- Talk about what Bob Bug's mixture might taste like. Ask your child, *Would you like to eat the mix? Why?*

- Find some words in the story with the *i* sound in them (*big, tins, tips, in, fig, mix, his*). Try to write *tins*. Say all the sounds in the word separately then write the letter that makes each sound.

Bob Bug has a big pan
and a lot of tins.

Bob cuts up a bun.

Bob tips in a pot of jam.

Bob cuts up a lemon, a melon and a fig.

Mix, mix, mix!
Bob rubs his tum.

Bob tips in a lot of nuts.
Mix, mix, mix!

Dad Bug says, "Yuk!"
Mum Bug says, "Yuk!"

But Bob Bug says, "Yum yum!"

About the author

Julia Donaldson, author of *The Gruffalo*, has captivated children all over the world with her lively and engaging stories.

Read with **Oxford** *Songbirds Phonics* have been carefully created by Julia to support children who are learning to read.

Julia Donaldson was born in 1948. She grew up in London and studied Drama and French at Bristol University. She worked for a few years in publishing and as a teacher, while also writing and performing songs and street theatre with her husband Malcolm, and writing and directing two musicals for children.

In 1993, one of her songs was made into a book, *A Squash and a Squeeze*. Since then she has written over two hundred books and plays for children and teenagers, including award-winning rhyming stories such as *Room on the Broom* and *What the Ladybird Heard*. Julia is one of the UK's best-selling authors.

Songbirds

By discovering and enjoying all the *Songbirds* collections, your child will build up and practise a secure knowledge of phonics and the confidence to sound out words to read.

Read the *Songbirds* collections in order to provide the perfect reading context for your child to practise sounding out words to read.

The fun and engaging activity books, *Alphabet Games* and *Phonic Games* provide further phonic practice and lots more opportunities for your child to talk about the stories.